EXTREME FEAR

Contents

Helen Chapman

Story illustrated by
Carl Pearce

Before Reading

Find out about

- Some extremely dangerous sports

Tricky words

- welcome
- bounce
- centres
- icicles
- instructor
- sledging

Text starter

There are lots of extreme sports and they are all dangerous! You might like to try ice climbing or white-water sledging, or even cave diving. But to be safe, you will need all the right gear!

Extreme Sports

Welcome to the world of extreme sports!
It's a world full of fun and danger.
Would you like to climb up a frozen waterfall, sledge down a white-water river, or dive deep down into an underwater cave?
You will need a lot of nerve ...
and quite a lot of gear!

Ice climbing is cool!

Can you climb up a waterfall?

Only if it is frozen!

That's what ice climbers do.

They climb up frozen waterfalls.

It can be fun but it is very dangerous.

You might fall, or your ice axe might
bounce off the ice and hit you in the face!

You don't live near a frozen waterfall? Then you can go ice climbing indoors! Some climbing centres have indoor ice walls. The ice on these walls can be one metre thick! Giant freezers keep the wall frozen. There are even icicles on it!

Extreme – but safe!

To keep safe when ice climbing:

- Never climb alone.
- Climb with an instructor.
- Tell someone where you are climbing.
- Tell someone how long you will be.
- Take your mobile phone.

It is also important to have all the right gear.

Don't try this sport if you don't like heights!

Got all your gear?
Helmet
to protect your head
Hat
to stop your ears
freezing off
Rope
Gloves
to stop your fingers
freezing off
Harness
Ice axe
Socks
to keep your
toes cosy
Crampons
to help your
boots grip
the ice

White-water sledging is wicked!

Have you ever tried body-boarding in the sea? White-water sledging is a bit like body-boarding, but instead of being in the sea, you go down very fast rivers. White-water sledging is very exciting. You speed around tight bends and go over bumpy bits, but hang on tight as you might even go over a waterfall!

White-water sledging is fun, but it can be dangerous. The water tries to rip the sledge from your grip. You might be swept off your sledge or hit your head on a rock. If you fall off, you might not be able to swim to the side.

Extreme – but safe!

To keep safe when white-water sledging:

- Never go sledging alone.
- Only sledge with an instructor.
- Tell someone where you have gone.
- Tell someone how long you will be.

It is also important to have the right gear.

Don't try this sport if you can't swim!

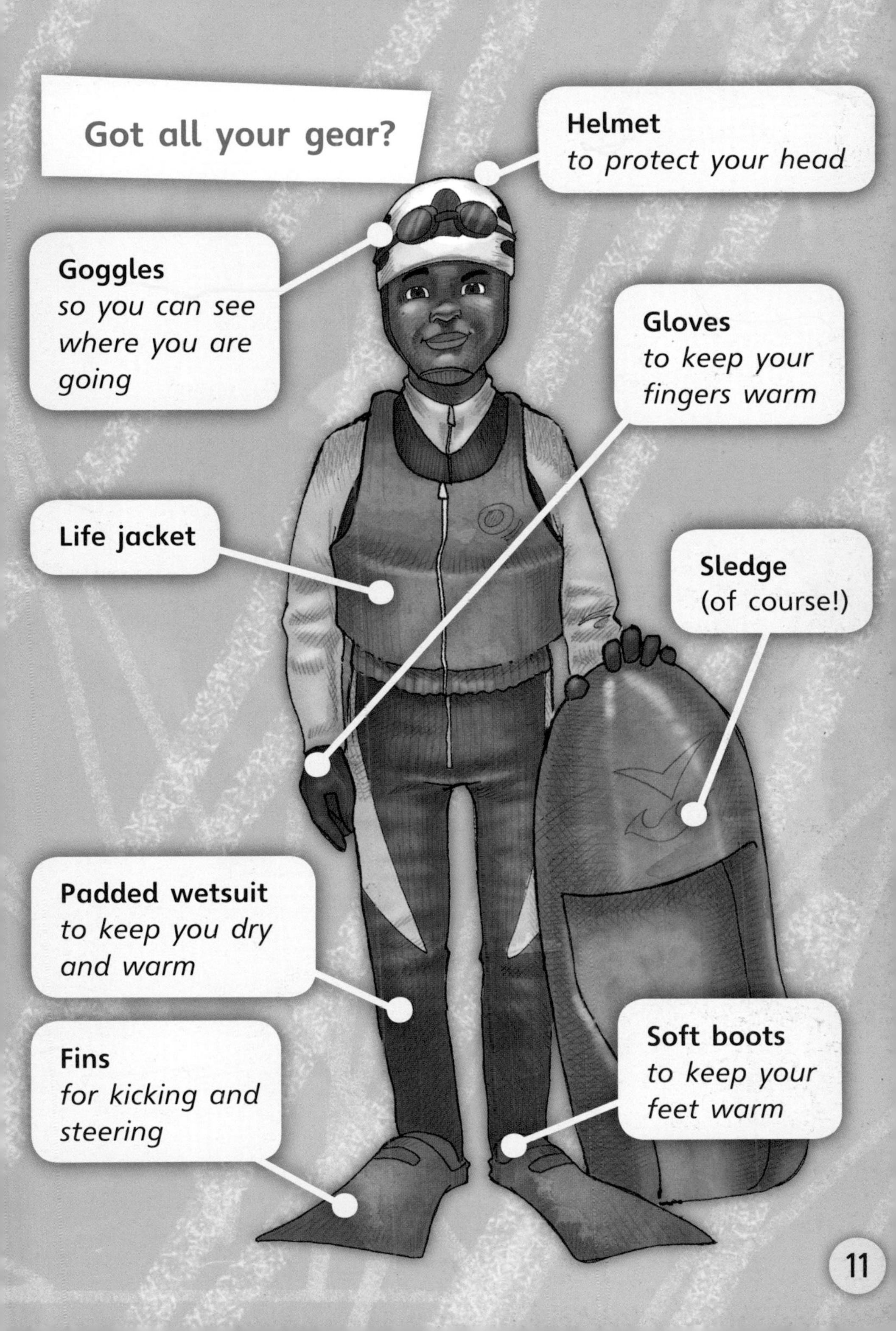
Got all your gear?
Helmet
to protect your head
Goggles
so you can see where you are going
Gloves
to keep your fingers warm
Life jacket
Sledge
(of course!)
Padded wetsuit
to keep you dry and warm
Fins
for kicking and steering
Soft boots
to keep your feet warm

Cave diving is crazy!

Cave divers like to visit deep, cold, dark caves. They dive thousands of metres under water.

But lots of things can go wrong:

- You can get lost.
- You can run out of air.
- You can stir up mud in the cave and then you can't see.

Sometimes, the water comes right up to the roof of the cave and you can't get out. If something goes wrong and you need to get out quickly, you must go back out of the cave the way you came in. Then you must swim up. Lots of divers panic and forget to do this.

Got all your gear?

Wetsuit with a hood

Mask
to help you to see

Scuba tanks

Fins
for kicking and steering

Lights
(always take two – just in case!)

Don't try this sport if you are afraid of the dark!

Quiz

Text Detective

- Which is an easier way to go ice climbing?
- Which extreme sport would you like to try?

Word Detective

- **Phonic Focus:** Unstressed vowels
  Page 3: Which letters represent the unstressed vowel in 'river'? (er)
- Page 9: Find a word meaning 'snatch'.
- Page 12: Find three adjectives describing 'caves'.

Super Speller

Read these words:

important being exciting

Now try to spell them!

HA! HA! HA!

Q Why did the water fall?

A Because it was scared of heights.

Before Reading

In this story

Karl

Adam

Miss Sharp

Tricky words

- abseiling
- instructor
- harness
- swarmed
- peered
- swollen
- phoned

Story starter

Karl and Adam were best friends. One summer, they went to an adventure camp. At the camp they could try all sorts of extreme sports, including abseiling. But Karl found out something at the cliff edge. He was afraid of heights.

Feel the Fear

Karl stood at the edge of the cliff and looked down.

"It's a long way down," he said.

"What did you expect?" laughed Adam. "We've walked slowly up and now we're going quickly down. That's what abseiling is all about!"

Karl looked over the edge again. He felt dizzy, as if he was going to fall. He stepped back quickly.

"I can't do this," he thought.

"Do you want to go first?" called Adam.

"No, it's OK. You go first," said Karl.

"I just need to check my helmet."

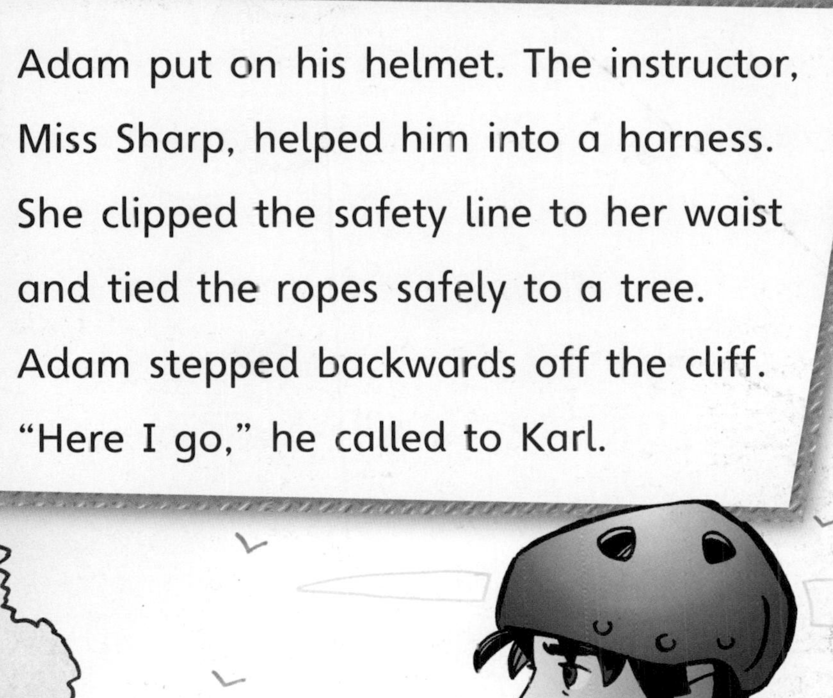

Adam put on his helmet. The instructor, Miss Sharp, helped him into a harness. She clipped the safety line to her waist and tied the ropes safely to a tree. Adam stepped backwards off the cliff. “Here I go,” he called to Karl.

"There's no way I can do that!" thought Karl.

Then he had an idea. While Miss Sharp was helping Adam, he would slip away. "Maybe Miss Sharp won't miss me," he thought. "Then I'll go back the way we came up. I can just pretend that I abseiled down."

Karl moved away from the cliff edge. There was a large rock and he sat down behind it. He could hear Miss Sharp giving Adam instructions.

"What a wimp I am!" he thought, and he picked up a loose stone and flung it at a nearby tree.

To Karl's surprise a black cloud rose up out of the tree. "What's that?" he thought. Then he heard a loud buzzing noise. "Bees," thought Karl. "My stone must have hit a bees' nest."

At that moment thousands of angry bees swarmed over his head.

Miss Sharp was slowly letting out the rope as Adam abseiled down the rock face. Without warning, the swarm of bees attacked. Miss Sharp screamed as the bees stung her face and hands.
She let go of her rope.

A yell came from below. It was Adam.
Karl ran to the edge of the cliff and
peered over. His head started to spin,
but he made himself look down.
"Are you OK?" he called to Adam.

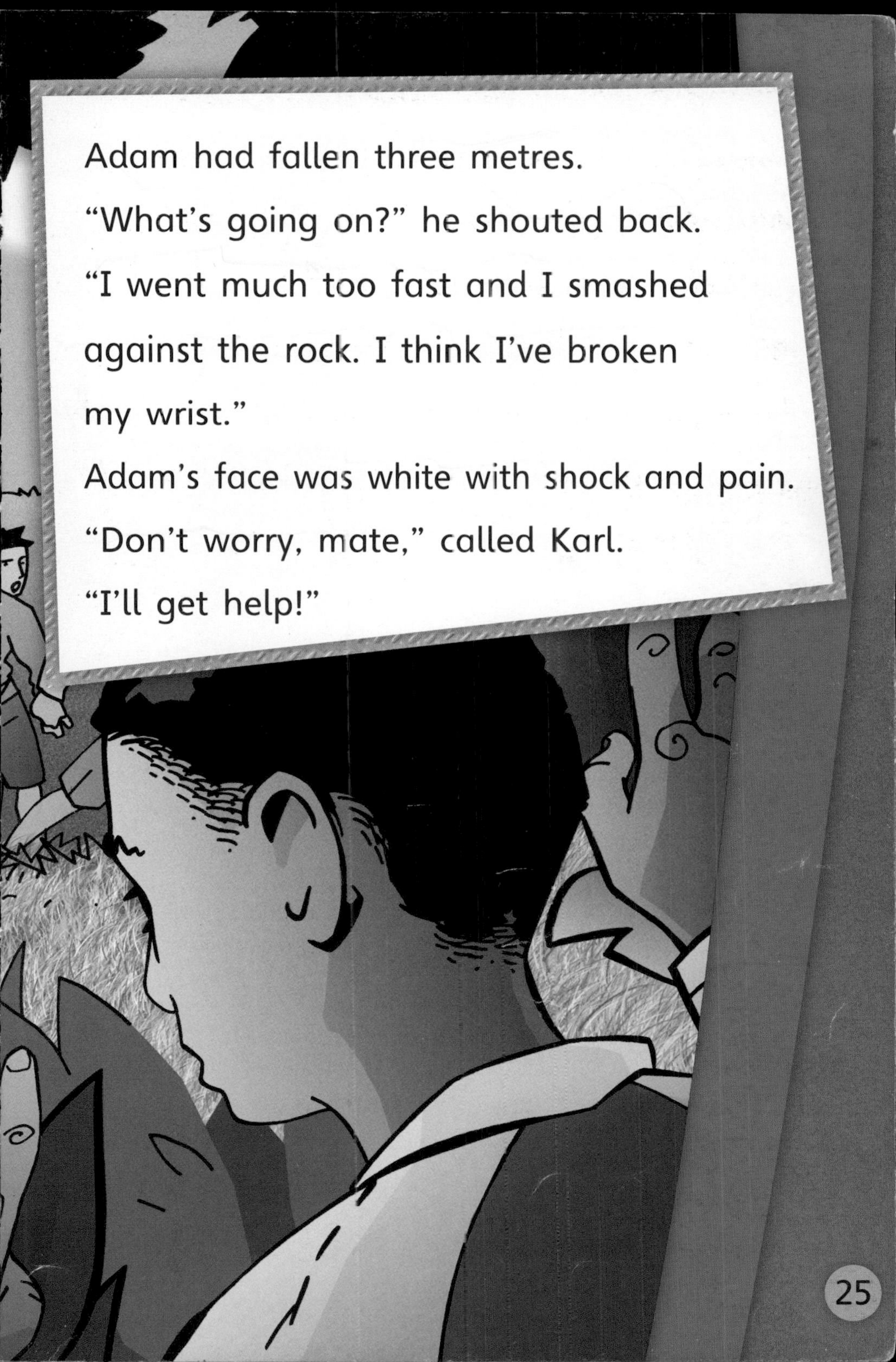

Adam had fallen three metres.

“What’s going on?” he shouted back.

“I went much too fast and I smashed against the rock. I think I’ve broken my wrist.”

Adam’s face was white with shock and pain.

“Don’t worry, mate,” called Karl.

“I’ll get help!”

What could Karl do? He couldn't climb down and Adam couldn't climb up.
"It's all my fault!" thought Karl.

Miss Sharp couldn't help Adam either. Her hands were too swollen. "We've phoned for help, but it could take them an hour," she said.
Karl knew Adam couldn't wait that long.

"You've got to hang on," Karl called down to Adam. But Adam had blacked out. His body hung limply.

Then Karl knew what he had to do.

His hands shook as he put on the helmet and harness. He tied the rope to the tree and clipped on the safety line.

"You're going to have to talk me down," he called to Miss Sharp.

"Stand with your face to the cliff, hold the rope tightly and don't look down," she said.

With a feeling of panic Karl stepped out off the cliff edge.

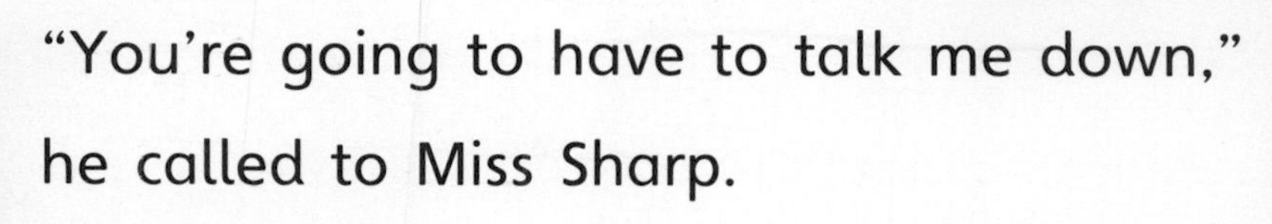

Stones skidded under his boots. He heard them crash a long way down.

"That will be me next," he thought.

Then Karl looked down. Big mistake! He felt so dizzy. His brain told him to move, but his body couldn't budge.

"I can't do this," he sobbed.

Then he saw Adam's limp body just below him.
"Wake up," called Karl, and he gently shook Adam. "Hold on to me with your good hand, and we can both go down slowly together."
It was hard work. Bit by bit, Karl and Adam inched their way down the cliff.

"I'm sorry," said Karl. "I was too chicken to abseil and I made the bees swarm."

"Yeah, but you did abseil in the end, didn't you?" said Adam. "You were really brave. But from now on you'd better behave – bee-have, get it?"

Karl groaned.

Quiz

Text Detective

- Why did Miss Sharp let go of the rope?
- Do you think Karl was a wimp?

Word Detective

- **Phonic Focus:** Unstressed vowels
  Page 19: Which letters represent the unstressed vowel in 'instructor'? (or)
- Page 22: Which word describes the bees?
- Page 27: Find the words which mean 'fainted'.

Super Speller

Read these words:

heard large stand

Now try to spell them!

HA! HA! HA!

Q Why do bees hum?

A Because they've forgotten the words.